P9-CEC-507

Somebody's Thinking of You

by

Rosalind Welcher

published by

Panda Prints, Inc.   New York

somebody's thinking of you

Somebody's awfully glad you're you

somebody thinks you're FUN to KNOW

somebody likes your smile

somebody likes the way you walk

somebody likes the way you talk

somebody likes your style

somebody likes to hear your voice

somebody likes to get your letters

somebody's sorry when you're feeling ill

somebody misses you when you're away

somebody thinks your jokes are funny

somebody's there if you want a shoulder
to cry on...

somebody's there to hold your hand

somebody's glad when nice things happen

somebody's sorry when things go wrong

somebody wants you to be happy

somebody hopes all your dreams
come true

somebody is me

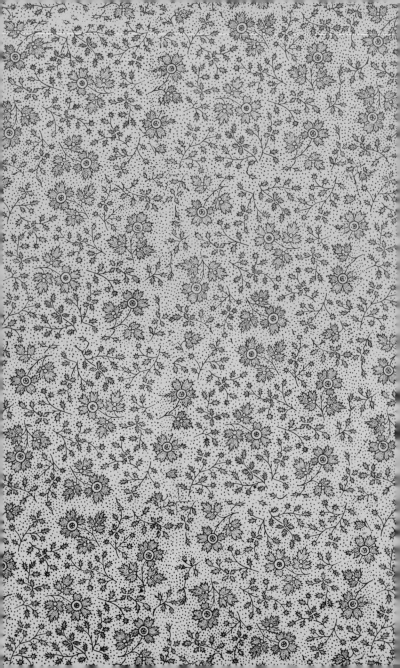